Yosemite National Park, CA

Crater Lake National Park, OR

Mesa Verde National Park, CO

Everglades National Park, FL

Yosemite National Park, CA

Mount Rushmore National Memorial, SD

THE NATIONAL PARKS PRESERVE ALL LIFE

 Wild Life — poster (WPA)

8 7 6 5 4 3 2

Grand Canyon National Park, AZ

Great Smoky Mountains National Park, TN

SEE AMERICA

UNITED STATES TRAVEL BUREAU

 Carlsbad Caverns, NM — poster (WPA)

Bryce Canyon National Park, UT

Manzanita Lake, CA — poster (WPA)

Zion National Park, UT (Red Canyon Route)

DEPARTMENT OF THE INTERIOR, NATIONAL PARK SERVICE

THE NATIONAL PARKS
PRESERVE WILD LIFE

 Preserve Wild Life – poster (WPA)

9 8 7 6 5 3 2 1

Tahoe National Forest, CA

U.S. DEPARTMENT OF THE INTERIOR

FORT MARION

NATIONAL MONUMENT

St Augustine, Florida

Glacier National Park, MT (Two Medicine Lake)

DON'T KILL OUR WILD LIFE

DEPARTMENT OF THE INTERIOR
NATIONAL PARK SERVICE

Don't Kill Our Wild Life — poster (WPA)

Joshua Tree National Park, CA

ZION NATIONAL PARK

U.S. DEPARTMENT OF THE INTERIOR

NATIONAL PARK SERVICE

 Zion National Park, UT — poster (WPA)

9 8 7 6 5 4 3 2

Yosemite National Park, CA

ACADIA NATIONAL PARK

U.S. DEPARTMENT OF THE INTERIOR

NATIONAL PARK SERVICE

Channel Islands National Park, CA

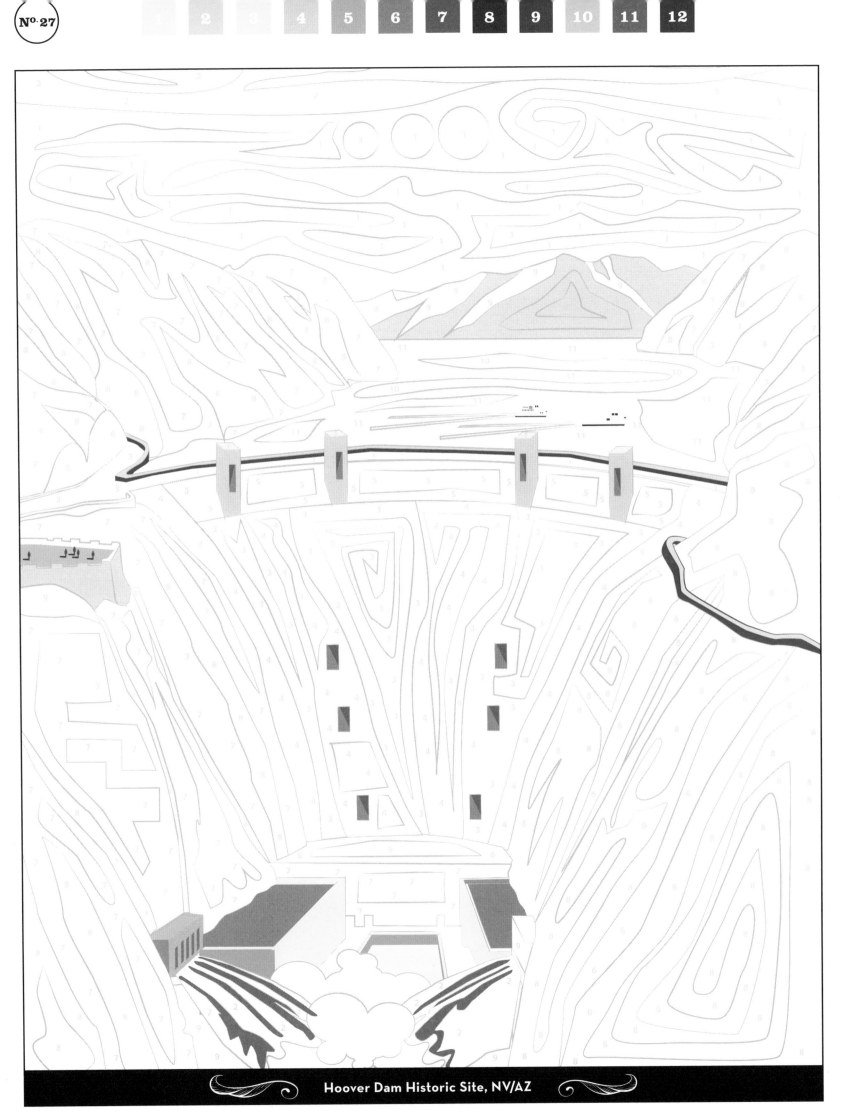

Hoover Dam Historic Site, NV/AZ

10 9 8 7 6 5 4 3 2 1

Badlands National Park, SD

Theodore Roosevelt and John Muir, Yosemite National Park, CA

Arches National Park, UT

8 7 6 5 4 3 2

Death Valley National Park, CA/NV

Canyonlands National Park, UT